Poems for Young and Old

With best wishes

David Farren

Poems for Young and Old

Published by The Conrad Press in the United Kingdom 2020

Tel: +44(0)1227 472 874

www.theconradpress.com

info@theconradpress.com

ISBN 978-1-913567-80-4

Typesetting and Cover Design by: Charlotte Mouncey, www.bookstyle.co.uk
With illustrations by David Farren,
The Conrad Press logo was designed by Maria Priestley.

Printed and bound in Great Britain by Clays Ltd, Elcograf S.p.A.

Poems for Young and Old

David Farren

In memory of my late parents William and Loraine and brother John. Always with me.

Contents

Timothy Platt - Part 1

Timothy Platt
Had a very big hat
He wore on top of his head
Although it was pink
His mother did think
That he shouldn't wear it in bed.

But though Timothy knew
It would make his mum blue
He slowly discovered a plan
When lights were out
There was no doubt
His careful thoughts began.

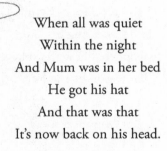

When all was quiet
Within the night
And Mum was in her bed
He got his hat
And that was that
It's now back on his head.

Paddy McGrew
Trod in some glue
And things became quite tricky
He couldn't wear his shoes and socks
For they had become quite sticky.

'What shall I do?'
He said to Sue
Who happened to be passing,
'I don't know' she quickly said
And couldn't stop her laughing.

So, home he went
To his house in Kent
Still pondering his fate,
He wondered how to explain
The reason he was late.

But Mum was there
And despite her stare
She wasn't very vexed
Because when Sue stopped laughing
She sent his mum a text.

The Grumpet

I must admit I never knew
There was a grumpet in the zoo.
'What's a grumpet?' I hear you say
'You don't see one of those each day.'

Well, a grumpet comes from over the sea
And often invites the monkeys to tea.
He's very tall and has long feet
And answers to the name of Pete.

His knobbly knees and curly hair
Make him look much like a bear,
But he's not a bear of that I'm sure
Because he has hands and not a paw.

So to bring this story to an end
Before it drives me round the bend,
Next time you visit to the zoo,
Make sure you visit Grumpet too!

Bedtime

When bedtime comes, I like to be
A pirate on the open sea.
I take my ship to distant shores
Find gold, diamonds and much more.
Fighting dragons, I'm so brave
Climbing mountains, down in caves.
My adventures just go on and on
And they are all just endless fun.

There was a time not long ago
I fought a dragon in the snow,
It was a struggle I must say
But to me it was just another day.
I become good friends with lords and kings
I fight with tigers, lions and things.
But my adventures end with Mum's call
'Get up Rufus it's time for school.'

Chocolate Cake

A friend of mine by the name of Jake
Is very fond of chocolate cake,
So, when he asks, 'Mum what's for tea?'
It's never what he hopes it'll be.
Sausages, pies, or even steak
Are not the same as chocolate cake.

So, one day Jake and I began some cooking
While we knew no one was looking.
Flour and eggs and milk in the pot.
Make sure the oven's hot
Add the chocolate and pop it in,
Now we let the cooking begin.

Out of the oven and left to cool
Jake and I patient on our stool.
One big slice and then another
Even better than made by Mother.
We even had the bowl to lick
Sadly, both Jake and I were very sick.

The Hefferklump

A hefferklump is a wonderous beast
Who's every meal is like a feast,
He feeds on grass and very tall trees
Which is why he has such knobbly knees.

He doesn't like to be seen
When he eats everything that's green.
He has four ears and seventeen toes
And a very long trunk instead of a nose.

He's kind to animals and friendly to man
And helps everyone as much as he can.
His very best friend lives over the road
In the house next door to a slippery toad.

He's so polite and never rude,
And very often shares all his food.
But most of all it must be said
He's very happy laying in bed.

Moon Journey

It seems to me that very soon
We'll buy a ticket to the moon,
And flying amongst the shining stars
There will be no need for motor cars.
It seems a long, long way to go
But at least there won't be any snow.

And as we'll be nearer the sun
I'm sure we will have lots of fun.
So, I'm reading about the solar system,
And hope that all my friends will listen
To all the things we didn't know
And special things that I can show.

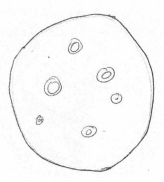

Millie's Grandad

A little girl called Millie
Thinks her grandad is very silly.
He puts things on his head
And wears his shoes in bed.

One day he was told,
By someone very bold,
His shoes were on the wrong feet a lot
He replied, 'they're the only feet I've got.'

He likes to eat chocolate and pies,
And is very fat so no surprise.
So nearly all his teeth have gone,
And some may wonder how that's done
But the reason is quite clear and stuff,
He didn't brush his teeth enough.

The Moon

Many people wonder why
There is a moon up in the sky.
It gets up when we go to bed
And disappears in day instead.
It looks from earth as though it slants
And doesn't have animals or plants.

Sometimes it hides some of its face
Or disappears without a trace.
And ever since time had begun
It has been known to hide the sun.

But if you look when the whole moon shows
You can see his eyes and even his nose.
He sits up high like a great big ball
I hope he never has a fall.
But would you tell me one thing please
Is it really made of cheese?

Nuxley Green - Part 1

Down in the woods near Nuxley Green
A strange creature is sometimes seen.
Neither man nor beast it seems to be
Least nobody says with certainty.
Some say he's tall and some that he's not
And one person said he looks rather hot!

So Nuxley Green is a popular place
And taking up all newspaper space,
So those who have seen this peculiar creature
In local newspapers and on TV feature.
But it's all very strange and maybe a game
That no two stories are ever the same.

There have been other stories over many years
Some of which may have reached your ears,
Of strange looking creatures occasionally seen
That are even stranger than Nuxley Green.
Abominable Snowman or Monster Loch Ness
But most people just couldn't care less.

So, before I finish this rather tall story,
A tale that I hope is not too gory,
Be sure if you go near Nuxley Green,
Which you can't do before you're sixteen,
Take a packed lunch and a camera as well
And you just might have a good story to tell.

The Boy from Aberystwyth - Part 1

The boy from Aberystwyth had a very itchy nose
And every time he sneezed his socks flew of his toes.
One day he sneezed so loudly
It shook his golden locks,
And Mum said, 'nothing for it,
We're going to the docs.'

The doctor shook his head and said,
In no uncertain terms
'We have to stop this sneezing,
Just think of all the germs.'
So, the boy from Aberystwyth did not start school next day
Instead, he started thinking of games that he could play.

So, with a dose of medicine
And instructions from the docs
He went to bed as usual
In his favourite Arsenal socks.
He curled beneath the blankets and sneezed and sneezed
and coughed,
He hadn't even bothered to brush his golden locks.

With a bottle of the mixture and a silver-plated spoon
His mum gave him his medicine and all so very soon
The boy from Aberystwyth in his favourite Arsenal socks,
Was sat down with some jelly, his feet upon a box.
'Back to school tomorrow' his mum had said with ease,
Just at that very moment the boy began to sneeze.

Grandma's Garden

Grandma loves her garden,
She keeps it very neat,
She makes holes for the bulbs
And covers them with peat.

She waters them each evening
Before she has her tea
She thinks it will look pretty
I'm sure you will agree.

And so the weeks go by
The plants begin to show
It really is amazing
How fast they seem to grow.

Colours now begin to blend
And Grandma clears the weeds
Thinking to herself 'next year
I'll buy some extra seeds.'

Grandad does get grumpy,
He thinks it is a sin
If Grandma puts her cuttings
In the wrong recycling bin.

Patmore Green

At the bottom of the garden
Of a house in Patmore Green
There is a long-told story
That a fairy's often seen.

Although I've never seen her
It's surely no surprise
That several who have witnessed
Just can't believe their eyes.

It has been said that she's quite small
No higher than a chair
Wings of course and a lovely face
And long, long golden hair.

I don't think she is alone
I think there might be others
Somebody who has seen her
Thinks she might have brothers.

Rita Babbage

Rita Babbage
Loved the cabbage
With her Sunday dinner,
She often ate
All on her plate,
Thinking she would be thinner.

But Rita knew
That even stew,
In reasonable portions,
Yes, even that
She'd not get fat
Or out of all proportion.

She often ran
With her friend Nan
And others she knew too
Sometimes fast
If she could last
And didn't lose her shoe.

Fit she was
And that's because,
Although she wasn't wealthy
She was so good
That all the food
She ate would make her healthy

Swimming

When you go swimming don't forget
There is no doubt you'll get very wet.
Brolly, wellies are no good
Though you might like a swimming hood.

Swimming makes you big and strong,
You can ask Annabelle to come along.
Sophie and Emma might like to come too
Then you'll be with all your crew.

Being all girls would be quite swell
Though you might like to ask your brother as well.
But no doubt if Rufus did come along
He'd bring Thomas, Hugo and Cameron.

Now when you've finished, and all got dressed
You can all pop along to Pizza Express.
All that swimming I'm sure has now made
Good time for pizza and lemonade.

The Friendly Giant

Long, long ago in a land far away
Lived a friendly giant by the name of Ray.
He was the leader of a friendly band,
Who were always ready to lend a hand,
To anybody whether friend or foe,
No matter how far they had to go.

Ray was kind and tried to be
A leader who had sympathy
With everyone who needed a hand,
He'd send his loyal and trusted band
To fix any problems his neighbours had
No matter if they were good or bad.

Ray was not his actual name
Nor was he using it just as a game,
In fact, his name was very long
It almost sounded like a song
The actual name that his mother gave him
Was Rayamondoconogorim.

So, Ray ruled his land and was always kind
Which is why I think you will always find
That if you treat everybody well
It will be quite easy for you to tell
That you are a nice person and so it will be too
That everyone you meet will be nice to you.

Rudolph

If Rudolph hadn't a big red nose
Santa wouldn't find us I suppose.
Would he have to use a light,
It would need to be very bright.
If he couldn't see any wall
Perhaps he wouldn't call at all.

Thank goodness then Rudolph's nose is red
Which means while you're tucked up in bed,
Santa can still find his way
And leave the toys for you to play.
So, keep being good and you will hear
Santa will be back next year.

Tommy Shinn

Tommy Shinn
Was very thin
He never ate his dinner,
So, he was told
As he got old
He'd grow up even thinner.

Tommy grew
And so he knew
He should eat all his meals,
All his food
Was very good,
And happier he feels.

Though Tommy ate
All on his plate
He tried to control his portions
That all he had
Would not be bad
Or make him out of proportion.

Kindness

Whatever future you may find
Remember always to be kind
To everyone you know or meet
Be sure to give a pleasant greet.

Not everybody is the same
But don't deserve to be called a name,
Though different they seem to you
They have the right to respect too.

Some are black and some are white
But equally they have the right
To live a life that's rich and dear
And be happy with no fear.

So, if someone you know is sad
Because they have been treated bad,
Do your best to make them see
They can live quite happily.

Jeremy Nish

Jeremy Nish
Loved to fish
He was happy by the water
He'd sit all day
On the river Tay
Much longer than he oughta.

His mother knew
If she cooked stew
It seldom would be eaten
For Jeremy
Came home for tea
Only when he felt beaten.

Fish bite
Day and night
So Jeremy was ready
Any time
With his line
Always very steady.

So Mother said
'Before your bed
Remember what to do
Get a pot,
To keep it hot,
And fill it with some stew.'

Grandad

Grandad's hair is silver
His teeth have nearly gone,
He sits in his chair all day
With his tea and a scone.

He talks about the good old days
When it hardly ever rained,
That how he's climbed up mountains
And the tigers that he's trained.

His jokes are never funny
Though often told again,
He laughs at them so loudly
It seems to be his plan.

He says he joined the army
When he was just a lad
He worked very hard at school
And never was he bad.

Maybe when I'm older
I'll be like him as well
And to my own grandchildren
Same tall stories I'll tell.

The Star

I saw a star up in the sky
And all I did was wonder why
How such a distant tiny light
Can seem to shine so very bright.

Are there streetlights on the stars?
Are there people there with cars?
How far away can they be
So that I can clearly see.

I think one day I may decide
To take a daring spaceship ride,
To visit stars and maybe soon
Pay a visit to the moon.

I might even ask my friend Jake,
The one who likes chocolate cake,
To join me on my special craft
Though others may sneer and laugh.

We will become a famous pair
To carry out such a brave dare,
And everyone the whole worldwide
Will look at us with enormous pride.

Dad's Chair

While Mum dusts around the house
And Dad sits in his chair,
Stuart plays with his train
And Alicia combs her hair.

Mum asks Dad if he could help
And perhaps to do a chore
But he says he's watching football
And they're just about to score.

'Things have got to change,' Mum said,
'It really is not fair,
That I do all the housework
And you sit in the chair.'

Dad said 'I'm always busy,
I have so much to do,
And I don't feel too well
I think I've got the flu.'

So Mum devised a cunning plan
She knew was quite a dare,
And when Dad got up next morning,
She was sitting in his chair.

Mum said to Dad 'You've things to do,
And you can make a jelly,
Because today is my day off
To watch football on the telly.'

Cecil's Toes

Whenever Cecil saw his toes
He had to grab hold of his nose,
For though I know I should not tell
They did have the most awful smell.

His mother bought him loads of soap,
Something that she'd really hope
Would help him end this sorry state
Before he got to 28!

Deodorants and special powder
Only made the problem louder,
So Cecil not to be outfoxed
Always wore his shoes and socks.

But then one day his mum declared
That though the smell came with feet bared,
Perhaps for a visit to the docs
He really should wear his new socks.

The doctor gave Cecil a tube of cream
And said he must keep his feet clean,
To try the lotion for about ten days
To get him through this smelly phase.

Ten days passed all too soon
And Cecil felt over the moon
No longer had he smelly feet
The sad affliction had been beat.

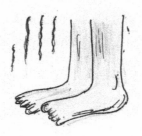

Cheese

Cheese, I hear, it's often said,
Should not be eaten near to bed.
It can result in dreadful dreams
And apparitions of figurines.
So take care with that evening snack,
Or it will surely get you back.

A light supper may be best
To ensure that your night-time rest
Is not disturbed by other things,
And will give you the sleep of kings.
A glass of milk and biscuit should do
So you can rest the whole night through.

Percy

Percy's nose was rather long,
And sometimes very runny,
But he did think it was wrong
That others thought it funny.

He sniffed and snuffled every day
And night-time was no better,
So the things that he wanted to say
He wrote down in a letter.

'Dear All' he said at the start
'I hope you all will listen,
I am telling you from my heart
About my problem that's persisting.'

'The nose I've got I've always had
Been with me since my birth,
But what makes me feel so sad
Is that others find it mirth.'

'Dear people please do try
To be more understanding,
And let all our lives go by
Differences withstanding.'

Training

I've often heard that an apple a day
Will surely keep the doctor away,
But I think that there is much more
To keeping this medic from your door.

Though fitness comes with what you eat
It's also how you use your feet.
So walk or run and you can tell
Exercise will keep you well.

This doesn't count for Grandads though
For I've no doubt that you will know,
That Grandads have no need to train
Their exercise is done by brain.

Advice and opinion is given a lot
Regardless, whether you want it or not,
They know about things old and new
And about what's false and what's true.

Grandads know the answers to be told,
They know everything, because they are old,
And if the queen needs something to endorse
She will ask the opinion of Grandad of course.

Timmy Piper

Timmy Piper surely knows
He shouldn't really pick his nose
His mother told him it was yuk
And he might get his finger stuck!

Mum said 'you will go to school
And you will simply look a fool
As all will ask you why you chose
To stick your finger in your nose.'

Remember too of many chores
Needed to be done in doors,
Like washing, eating and playing games
Will likely never be the same.

So the moral of this snotty tale
From which I hope you will prevail,
Use your fingers like the rest of the globe
And not just as a nasal probe.

Lockdown

If you have to stay indoors
And spend your time mopping floors,
Just think of all the times ahead
And take the chance to lay in bed.
For time will pass and you will see,
We'll all view things differently.
Perhaps we all must appreciate
The world can live without the hate
For race, religion and the rest
We don't consider to be the best.

For my part I have to say
I have no problem every day
To do as little as I dare
And stay sitting in my chair.
But I have a strict exercise regime
Which I have included in my scheme.
I often break out in a sweat,
Though it hasn't happened much as yet,
That it might be too difficult to shirk
And I might be forced to do housework.

Runner Bean

How many times have you seen
The fastest ever runner bean?
Or in your travels heard about
A tasty healthy Brussel sprout?

I wonder even if in Winnipeg
They can buy a nice Scotch egg.
But most of all a total squeeze
Of a large plate of mushy peas.

Maybe you've sat on a log
And nibbled at a nice hot dog,
Or looked up to the sky and wish
Perhaps you'd see a flying fish.
But I wish you a rainbow to behold
And follow to a pot of gold.

The Practors

Mr Practor
Drove his tractor
Round and round his farm.
Mrs Practor
Had a fracture
At the bottom of her arm.

'So,' she said,
When she jumped in bed
'I won't get up tomorrow,'
'Oh dear,' he said
When he fell in bed
'That really brings me sorrow.'

'Cows,' he said
As he rose from bed
'Need milking twice today'
'Oh,' she said
As she turned in bed
'There's nothing more to say.'

Mr Practor
Didn't drive his tractor
Round and round his farm.
Mr Practor
Milked the cows
So they didn't come to harm.

Windrush

Long, long ago from a place far away,
People came to England to stay.
To nurse, to drive and even to brush
They all became known as the great Windrush.

England had been battered by a terrible war,
A country that needed people and more
To help to clear, restore and rebuild
A country whose destiny had been fulfilled.

They came in their hundreds to answer the call
By promises of welcome, security and all,
And though their welcome was not always clear
They toiled and justified their presence here.

The jobs they took were not the first pick
They drove our buses and nursed our sick,
And though there are many who couldn't care less
They became the backbone of our NHS.

Now the country is facing another great war
And troops are required on every floor,
So many from countries other than ours
Will once again unleash their magical powers.

And when we complain about our own lot
Remember those that the country forgot,
Those aliens we often consider to be less
Will once again bolster our own NHS.

Billy's Feet

Billy had enormous feet and boots that didn't fit.
He couldn't walk very far and often had to sit,
Until his feet had a rest and shoelaces were loosened
It was difficult for Billy who found walking quite gruesome.

Now Billy thought that his large feet would help him
water skiing
But he didn't know where to start and he often had the feeling,
In order he could fulfil his dream and not feel quite a dope
He'd need to find a beach which had a sea that had a slope.

It wasn't till he was told by someone he knew well
Apart from having feet so large they also rather smell,
So instead of looking for a sloping sea or slanting Scottish lochs
He invested very wisely in a brand-new pair of socks.

Grandad's Chair

Grandad's chair is big, it's also very deep
He's always sitting in it and often falls asleep.
He sits to watch the telly and listen to the news
And has been known to sit there whenever Chelsea lose.

He doesn't go to work now that he's retired
Knowing that his expertise is no longer required.
But he always keeps busy trying to decide
If something needed doing how quickly he could hide.

He thinks his chair is comfy, the best one in the flat
But he's the only one who's thinking is like that.
He sometimes does get grumpy and nearly has a fit
If he finds that someone else has been sitting in it.

Dreams

Where are my dreams when I get out of bed,
Are they somehow still in my head?
Perhaps they have drifted far, far away
Or don't survive for long in the day.

Has somebody else stolen my dream
While I was sleeping and couldn't be seen.
Or has it simply faded and gone
Until I can find another one?

Sometimes my dreams are very bright,
Sometimes they are the same each night,
But eventually they all drift away
Like a feather on a breezy day?

I do have dreams while I'm awake
A future plan that I must make,
For a life that to me is kind
And my true destiny I will find.

Tiddles

Tiddles the cat
Was very fat,
He ate too many mice.
He loved to eat
Anything meat,
So now he's paying the price.

His owner Jewel
Was not a fool,
She saved money not buying right
But sad to say
In every way
It's her fault this terrible plight.

Proper food
Would do him good,
Without the need for mice
Jewel should get
Food for her pet,
That would make him rather nice.

Paddy McGrew - Part 2

Not long ago, you will recall,
The terrible fate that did befall
Upon our friend Paddy McGrew
Who came unstuck in a pool of glue.

Well, I regret that I have to say
That wasn't his only unlucky day,
And since that most regretful fate
There is another memorable date.

Now Paddy was really a happy lad
And seldom was he very bad,
But not too long after the pot of glue
He had a problem at the zoo.

With Mum and Dad on a day out
Paddy could not help but shout,
In excitement with all that he saw
The lions, tigers and much more.

But some of the animals like to sleep
And many of them are quiet as sheep,
So to hear a boy making so much fuss
Would upset nearly all of us.

Now Brutus in his monkey cage
Was just now at that terrible age,
He thought that it would be great fun
To see if he could make Paddy run.

Just as the family passed his cage
Brutus pretended to be in a rage,
He roared and gave his chest a thump
Which made poor Paddy really jump.

Paddy ran faster than he ever had
Quickly followed by Mum and Dad,
Who told Paddy as straight as they could
That being too noisy is not very good.

Grandma's Hair

Grandma likes to wash her hair at least three times a week,
Grandad thinks she shouldn't but doesn't like to speak.
He thinks that if he tells her, it will surely make her shout,
For washing far too often will make her hair fall out.

'Your hair' he said, while stepping back 'is full of natural oil,
And washing it too often is bound to make it spoil.'
It does smell nice and looks a treat as green as emerald,
But it wouldn't be quite as nice if it made Grandma bald.

Grandma has then decided completely by herself,
There might be too much shampoo upon the bathroom shelf.
'I have now decided, three times perhaps won't do,
So I'll just do it twice a week and then I'll dye it blue.'

Nana's Knitting

Click clack, click clack
Nana's knitting a lovely hat,
It might be blue it might be red
But it will fit on somebody's head.

Next time it could be a scarf
Or maybe something to make you laugh,
Whatever it is please say out loud
'It's lovely' and make Nana proud.

She likes to think it keeps her fit
'You use your brain whenever you knit,
Knitting patterns aren't easy you know,
And I had to learn to sew.'

Knit one, purl two
Not the easiest thing to do,
And if you happen to drop a stitch
It won't be the only hitch.

So hold those arms out and wide
Don't let them drop down to your side,
While Nana winds the wool in a ball
Ready to knit jumpers for all.

Timothy Platt - Part 2

Now Timothy worked very hard at school
Proving to all that he was no fool,
He quickly learned to read and write
And completed his homework every night.

He worked so hard his teachers knew
That he would certainly be among the few
Whose life would become a success,
Despite his sometime peculiar dress.

Although it didn't happen a lot
They wondered if Timothy had lost the plot
When he would make the whole school chat
About his appearance in his favourite hat.

But maybe his hat was just for joy
And soon he became the school head boy.
He worked very hard and now he had grown,
And how those school years had flown.

Grandma's Breakfast

For juice, Grandma seems to think
She'll only drink grapefruit if it's pink.
Apple juice and a tropical flavour
Never have they been in favour.

She has a glass almost every morning
Though she is still a lady yawning,
Followed by a slice of toast
With marmalade she likes the most.

No fry up for her Sunday brunch,
For then it's far too close to lunch,
But even though the morning's late
Still its juice then toast on a plate.

Spring, summer and winter too
Nothing else will seem to do,
And if the marmalade's a bit lumpy
It's sure to make Grandma grumpy.

So, if Grandma ever comes to stay,
Which I know she will another day,
Make sure the juice is really pink
For nothing else will do, I think.

Nuxley Green - Part 2

For all those who didn't care less
It's now been seen in the national press,
For many doubted it would be seen
The mystery creature of Nuxley Green.
But somebody with camera and time
Is sure they've made a remarkable find.

This new information came to light
By someone who spent many a night,
Waiting and hoping beyond all doubt
That the mystery would soon be found out.
He says that he has many a clue
But he is the only one who knew.

I just think it all rather funny
And maybe he has been offered money,
To make sure that to Nuxley Green
Many frequent visitors will be seen.
I'm really not sure he has information
To be of great interest to the rest of the nation.

And so many newspapers will be sold
For the same old story frequently told,
And no doubt still with many a smirk
The publicity caused just might work,
And many a stranger will come to The Green
Not knowing whatever might be seen.

The Boy from Aberystwyth - Part 2

The boy from Aberystwyth, though we never knew his name,
Found his never-ending sneezing was never quite the same.
Of course, he sneezed
With greatest ease
And still had golden locks
But the one thing missing was his favourite Arsenal socks.

So now that sneezing is no longer an affliction,
The wonder is what happened to his Arsenal addiction,
No longer was he wearing his long most favoured socks
Not since that famous visit that took him to the docs.
The doctor hadn't told him his socks would make him sneeze
Even though he wore them well above his knees.

Now I don't want to sound as though I'm telling tales
But it is rather strange to find an Arsenal fan in Wales,
I hear they prefer rugby and like to sing a bit
Often while in chapel and sometimes down the pit.
So maybe he decided that rugby was his game
And wearing Arsenal socks would never be the same.

The Vicar - Part 1

The vicar's coming for tea tomorrow
And so is Aunty Pat,
She says she'll be bringing a chocolate cake,
And be wearing her brand-new hat.

We think the vicar will probably grumble
About the lack of suitable jumble
To be sold next week at the parish fete
He seems to think we're a little late.

But we'll tell him not to worry
For there is no real great hurry
There's plenty time still to go
And we'll put on a marvellous show.

Clothes with fashion out of date
Cups, saucers, mugs and plates
Everything no longer wanted hence
Will now be sold for just a few pence.

As for Auntie's brand-new hat
We really hope and pray for that,
For should it get mixed with the jumbles
It won't just be the vicar who grumbles.

Home

Many people like to be
Out in the country or down by the sea,
Although those people love to roam
I prefer to be at home.

At home I can sit and rest,
Watch telly if I think that best,
Read a book or have a look
At how to draw or even cook.

Now please don't think I might be lazy
Or even perhaps a little crazy,
This is the way I like to be
And the way that I'm happy.

Of course, I did once go to work
Sitting down like an office clerk,
But that of course was not the same
Now's a totally different game.

Start at nine and work till five
Busy like bees in the hive,
Stop for lunch at half past one
Really didn't feel like fun.

So many years at somebody's will
Earning money to pay all the bills,
Council tax and of course rent
Now I'm paid by the government.

Pension small but show no greed
As long as enough to clothe and feed,
But one advantage of getting old
I don't have to go out in the cold.

Football

The doctor said when I'm ill
To go to bed and take a pill,
Sleep and rest and in a while
Once again I'll start to smile.

Though my bed is nice and warm
And I'll not come to any harm,
I know that when friends come to call
I'm not allowed to play football.

Now football is my favourite game
So the time will not be the same,
It will be nice to lay in bed
But I'd rather be playing football instead.

Perhaps tonight when I dream
I'm playing for my favourite team,
And as the football match unfolds
I'll score the greatest winning goal.

A few days later I'm feeling well
So I'm sure that you can tell
From early morning till it's dark
I'm playing football in the park.

Penelope Klopp - Part 1

Penelope Klopp
Loved to shop
She treated them as her fun days,
She never knew
What to do
When shops were closed on Sundays.

Shoes and socks
Things in a box
Filled up every known corner
Everyone thought
That she ought
To change her name to Jack Horner.

Filling up drawers
Hanging on doors
The things she bought were plenty
Curtain hooks
Cookery books
And pictures of the gentry.

One day she
Delightedly
Heard about Sunday hours,
Out of the blue
Now she knew
Her pounds had even more powers.

Will she shop
Or will she stop
Everyone was asking the question
'No,' she said
Shaking her head,
'That is a terrible suggestion.'

Clouds

All those clouds up in the sky
Send different pictures to my eye.
Sometimes I see a growling bear
Then a man with curly hair.

I don't know why it seems to be
That others see things differently,
When I saw the growling bear
My friend saw a jumping hare.

Some clouds are purely white,
Darker when seen at night,
But when you see them black and grey
It's not going to be a very nice day.

The breeze pushes them gently along,
Provided that it is not too strong,
Changing pictures all the time
Just like a celestial pantomime.

Grandma Rules, OK?

Grandma said to Grandad, 'it really is no good
I do all the shopping and you eat all the food.
I have to do the washing and clean around the place
While you just sit there with a grin upon your face.'

But Grandad had an answer that he quickly gave,
'You really don't understand I have to be so brave,
My job here is not easy I have no time for blinking
While you do all the work and I do all the thinking.'

'But what is so important, you always have to think,
And so time consuming that you can't even blink?'
But once again the answer was given straight away
'I could explain it to you, but it would take all day.'

Then Grandad tried to insist his job was not so easy
But he always tried to stay so very bright and breezy.
Then while sipping tea and munching on a bun,
Grandad said that Grandma should get the housework done.

Martin

Martin was a foolish child, or so his mother said,
He never really combed his hair and wore his socks in bed.
'Martin, that will not do,' she often had to say
It seems that he would do things wrong nearly every day.
But there could be little doubt of that I am quite sure
That Martin's little problems his mother would endure.

She never raised her voice and never would she scold,
Though she often said Martin's antics really made her old.
She treated him with patience and never did get cross
As Martin did as he was told and knew she was the boss.
'You're not a child forever,' was frequently repeated,
And memories of a foolish child will surely be deleted.

So years went by and so we saw a not so foolish Martin
He always combed his hair each day and had a very fine parting.
He polished his shoes frequently, and as told for many years
Made sure when he was washing to clean behind his ears.
His shirts were always very crisp and looked as good as new,
Martin's sharp appearance was bettered by just a few.

So Martin had listened to all his mother said
From first thing in the morning until his time for bed.
The moral of this story which needed to be told
You're not a child forever and one day will be old.
So learn as much as you can while in your early years
Then growing much older will not carry any fears.

Grandma's Ears

Grandma didn't believe that her hearing wasn't right,
That's why she had the telly very loud every night.
We told her very often the volume was too high
But she just wouldn't listen as much as we did try.

Now Grandma does wear glasses to help her poor old eyes
So when offered a free hearing test it was not a big surprise,
She thought that if she had the test then all would surely see
Her hearing would be perfect and as good as you and me.

Oh dear, she had the test and it was a big surprise,
Grandma's hearing needed help just like her poor old eyes.
So now she can hear most everything we say
Because she fits her hearing aids every single day.

Timothy Platt - Part 3

Some time ago we had a chat
About Timothy and his enormous hat,
But time we know has surely flown
And Timothy has now really grown.

He now stands at six feet two,
And that's even without his shoe,
But despite growing and all of that
He's still very fond of his favourite hat.

He doesn't wear the hat in bed
Just like his mother once said,
Instead he keeps it locked away
To only wear on holiday.

But now because he is so grown
It's hats for which he has become known,
For now, within a very short hop
You will arrive at Timothy's shop.

Hats of every style and colour
Piled on top of one other,
Bring customers from far and wide
Which fills our Timothy full of pride.

Paddy McGrew - Part 3

I'm sure you remember the story often told
About Paddy McGrew and mishaps that unfold,
That things became sticky around a pool of glue,
And even more scary on a visit to the zoo.

Well now I have the pleasure to give a new report
All about Paddy and his newfound love of sport.
Perhaps those little mishaps in Paddy's early years
Gave him the confidence to overcome his fears.

Now it may seem that Paddy was once ungainly
That any mishaps would happen to him mainly,
But some of his friends were not always right
And some of them also became quite a sight.

Paddy's good friend called Barney McLoud
Was also known to be rather too loud,
But although it was Paddy who came to the fore
Barney's mishaps seemed to happen much more.

There was a time when Barney was out
That he and Paddy began to shout,
And older people who were all very near
Said they deserved a clip round the ear!

But Paddy's Mum discovered a good idea
Which she said Barney also might like to hear,
They were both very happy making such noise
They could give their support to the football boys.

So now every weekend and sometimes more
You'll hear them both shouting in row thirty-four,
Singing their songs and shouting out loud
Amongst an almost capacity crowd.

Daisy

Daisy said she had a cold,
It made her feel so very old.
Her eyes were runny, her nose was too,
She couldn't bend to tie her shoe.
She took a pill and went to bed,
'Now you rest,' her mother said.

Next day Daisy woke at eight,
Mother made her bed all straight,
'No school for you,' Mother said
'It's best another day in bed.'
'Starve a fever, feed a cold,
Or so that's what I have been told.'

'How would a boiled egg do?
I think that might be best for you.'
But Daisy didn't really care
And snuggled to her teddy bear.
Soon she was back to sleep,
'That boiled egg will have to keep.'

Feeling better at half past two,
At least she hadn't got the flu,
And so a bowl of chicken soup
Would help her body to recoup,
And by the end of this week
Daisy will be back at her peak.

Penelope Klopp - Part 2

Penelope Klopp
Who loved to shop
Found lockdown very bad,
She had to stop
And couldn't shop
Which made her very sad.

Money saved
Spending waived,
Did not improve her mind,
For she knew,
Feeling blue,
What bargains she could find.

Penelope thought
Things she bought
She could also buy online,
But she knew
As we do
That was not so fine.

Half the joy
Of any ploy
Was searching for a bargain,
Any shop
In just a hop
Could satisfy her plan.

Reluctantly
She had to see
How online shopping went,
Not the same
A different game
She never was content.

Months pass
Now at last
Penelope can start to shop,
With the hope
She will cope
And shopping will not stop.

The Vicar - Part 2

The vicar did come to tea,
And so did Aunty Pat.
She did bring a chocolate cake
And was wearing her brand-new hat.

The vicar did complain a bit
That things were not quite right,
The lack of suitable jumble
Had given him quite a fright.

We did manage to calm him down,
With several slices of cake,
And made him feel much better
Telling all the plans we'll make.

There was no need for him to fret
For lots of jumble came,
But I have no doubt next year
His mood will be the same.

The jumble sale I have to say
Left no one in the lurch,
And what of course we did achieve
Gave more funds to the church.

One thing that was concerning
About our Aunty Pat,
But I'm very pleased to report
No mishaps with her hat!

Parliament

They sit on green benches all in a row
From the gallery you can see them below,
Two teams of different colours one red and one blue
All of them claiming to represent us too.

They shout at each other and all make a fuss
They seem just like children on the morning school bus.
'Bravo' they shout, and wave papers high,
It does make you wonder if good manners apply.

Questions often asked but answers never straight
Really makes you worry about the nation's fate.
There are other teams one orange one green,
And some from up north who don't want to be seen.

So every five years or earlier it would seem
People can vote for their favourite team.
But to some it might seem rather mean,
You can only vote if you've reached eighteen.

Nan

In a pot
Nan forgot
To fill it up with water,
Pot soiled
Potatoes spoiled,
No dinner for her daughter.

No pot
So what
Could she cook for Daisy?
Not hot
Without a pot
Would people think her lazy?

Cupboard bare
Nothing there
She wondered where to look,
No food
No good
Nothing she could cook.

But then
She began
To think she'd earn a pardon,
If she
Could see
Something in the garden.

Oh dear
Right here
Lettuce and tomatoes plenty,
Nan could
And would
Not care her cupboard's empty.

The Boat

I had a boat
That wouldn't float
It had holes in the bottom,
I did hope
That plugged with soap
My fear could be forgotten.

But I felt
Soap would melt
And we would all get wetter,
So I thought
That I ought
To think of something better.

In a while
I did smile
It wouldn't cause pollution,
If I could
Find some wood,
And nails, it was the solution.

Tip tap
Rat tat
Nailed wood on the boat,
Now sure
Even more
Certain it will float.

Silly me
Didn't see
Nails wouldn't fix the boat,
Holes galore
Even more
And still the craft won't float.

Blaxton Mews

At the top of a hill near Blaxton Mews
People come to enjoy the views,
But what those people do not know
Is what the tour books do not show.
For hidden there, or very near,
There is a tale you might like to hear.

The tale begins many years ago,
But very few are in the know,
About the mystery that did unfold
Apparently when the weather was cold.
For one dark night in deepest snow
Very strange footprints were on show.

What could it be with such strange feet
That don't appear in the summer heat?
Those who had heard the story told
Did not venture out when it was cold,
So only the few who ventured out
Would know what the story was all about.

The story was told by local folk,
Though many considered it just a joke,
But, of course, as always there were some
Who really believed that a yeti had come.
But the mystery was traced to a kangaroo
Who frequently escaped from the local zoo.

Grandad's Chores

Grandad does the washing up
When Grandma cooks the dinner,
Grandad thinks the exercise
Will make him get much thinner.
The plates are very heavy
He scrubs them one by one,
He thinks he will soon finish
But it's really not much fun.

The dishes pile up higher
Knives and forks all shine,
Grandad keeps on working
While Grandma pours her wine.
He hopes he soon will finish
And all his chores are done,
Until he gets instructions
To put the kettle on.

Now the kettle's boiling
With cups of tea to make,
He receives further instructions
For a slice of carrot cake.
Grandad does enjoy a slice
And then he has to say
While he enjoys a second slice
'Towards my five a day'

Adrian Hogg

Adrian Hogg
Had a very big dog
He took for walks each day,
His lead was long
And Adrian strong
So his pet could not run away.

In the park
Even when dark
Adrian was fond of his pet,
He'd hold on tight
Every night
Even when weather was wet.

Every day
Come what may
He'd walk for miles with his friend,
He'd know
Even in snow,
It's exercise that he 'd recommend.

Adrian said
While laying in bed,
'I do enjoy walking much more,
But I know
Even in snow,
I have only two legs he has four.'

Food

Grandad doesn't like to cook,
He'd much rather read a book,
Or sit in his chair and wonder why
Elephants swim and pigs can't fly!

The pastime that he likes the most
Is breakfast with his tea and toast,
He'll spend this time deep in thought
Keeping active as a last resort.

Toast all eaten and teapot drained
He feels that nothing will be gained,
Unless he thinks and gets a hunch
Of what he might like for his lunch.

Lunch time seems a very long wait
Until he can see another plate,
And finally, in order to please
It's toast again this time with cheese.

Another wait and dinner's done
Waiting really is no fun,
But this time the plate's piled up high
Mashed potato, peas and pie.

And so a day finishes once more
And sleeping Grandad starts to snore,
No doubt his dreams will not bring sorrow
As he dreams about his food tomorrow.

The Clock

An old clock against the wall,
Very thin and very tall,
Hands and face to tell us all
When it's time we went to school.
His job has lasted many years
Through happy times and times for tears,
His pendulum swings with such power
He chimes to us at each new hour.

What happenings has he seen
Always polished always clean?
For many years he stood and saw
Friends and strangers through the door,
Family young and family old,
Long known stories often told,
And so with every echoing chime
Our faithful friend makes clear the time.

No doubt he'll stand for years to come
On sentry duty for our home,
And all the people we know so well
Will wonder what secrets he could tell,
Of things he's seen and voices heard
But never uttering a single word.
He sees us through hot days and cold
A face that never will grow old.

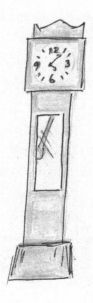

Cooking

So I could cook
I read a book
Which told me what to do,
How to mix
How to fix
And make a lovely stew.

First I shop
Then I chop
Potato, carrot and leek
In a pot,
Quite a lot
And gravy mustn't be weak.

Is it lamb
Or is it ham?
Both are tasty to me,
But I know
Just for show
I've invited friends for tea.

Friends came
Just the same
We all had a lovely dinner,
Must say
For today
Just won't make me any thinner.

Sweets

Pete said to Joe
'I've got to go,
I need to buy a jacket,'
Joe said to Pete
'Have a sweet,
I've got another packet.'

So Joe and Pete
Had a sweet,
And another two or three,
Pete said to Joe
'I've got to go,
It's nearly time for tea.'

Home they went
Time well spent,
But no new jacket for Pete,
He was told
He'd be cold
All for the sake of a sweet.

Orange Squash Shampoo

Grandma had an itchy head
And scratched it all the time,
Grandad said to wash it
In orange squash and lime.

Grandma said it wouldn't work
And all would think her barmy,
But Grandad said he knew it would
He learned it in the army.

Grandad then insisted
That all he said was true,
And Grandma's hair was not the same
Since the day she dyed it blue.

So with a bottle of squash
And a lime cut into two,
Grandma thought it might be
Just the thing to do.

She mixed the two together
A little at a time,
Then tried just orange squash
And later on just lime.

Grandad wasn't happy
That this would just not do,
She really had to wash her hair
With the mixture of the two.

So finally Grandma decided
To follow Grandad's pleas,
But now it smells so sweetly
She's pestered by the bees.

The Ghost

I think I may have seen a ghost
Eating lots of jam and toast,
As he swallowed, I could see
He hadn't really noticed me.
I turned to call my sister Clare
And suddenly he wasn't there.

I wonder if he'll come again
And if he will do just the same.
It seems that what he likes the most
Is lots and lots of jam and toast.
But though I know that I will stare,
I wonder, is he really there?

His appearances it may seem
Only happen when I dream,
But of that I'm not quite sure
And hope he will appear once more.
I leave some toast and I start yawning
But it's still there come the morning.

So maybe it is just a dream
And he will never again be seen,
But I will often wonder why,
As I look up and see the sky,
If he will visit me once more
So Clare will believe I really saw.

Anthony Bold

This is the tale of Anthony Bold
Who awoke one morning with a terrible cold,
His nose was runny, his eyes were too,
He really didn't know what to do.

He should be going to school but instead
His mother decided he should stay in bed,
With mugs of hot lemon and a warm duvet
She hoped his cold would soon go away.

Another day passed and his nose was so red
Meant there was no choice but to stay in his bed.
Although all the lemon had made him quite mellow
He was a little worried it might turn him yellow!

So as the days passed and Anthony knew
At least that he hadn't developed the flu,
And as he started to feel so very cool
He looked forward to returning to school.

So very much better and life back as it was,
Anthony felt happy and that was because
He'd meet all his friends and continue to be
Very hardworking and very happy.

Sharing

There was a boy
Who had a toy
A present he got for his birthday,
He didn't share
And didn't care
But wanted to play it his way.

Surely he should,
If he was good
Learn to share his things,
He would know
It would show
That a happier life begins.

If you share
Show you care,
And all will think you are kind.
If you don't
Then you won't
Find friendships to you bind.

One Shoe

Jennifer Pugh
Lost a shoe
And didn't know what to do,
She asked a chum
And asked her mum
If they could give her a clue.

She hopped along
Singing a song
And everyone gave funny glances,
Jennifer knew
Only a few
Would think it was one of those dances.

At last
Time passed.
And finally Jennifer stopped,
Home now,
Wondering how
Many times she had hopped.

Cousin Pete

Pat put on a wonderful spread
Cheese, ham and piles of bread.
Plenty for all to see and eat,
Especially for cousin Pete,
Whose appetite was known to be
Not just big but exceptionally.

Pete was known in days gone by
To eat more than just one pie
Several sandwiches and many cakes,
And various puddings and other bakes.
So I'm sure it won't be a surprise
That this is the man who ate all the pies.

Now Pete was certainly not fat,
And he was very proud of that,
It's just he didn't seem to care
He ate much more than just his share.
So to make sure all got enough to eat
They'd start before their cousin Pete.

The Letter

The government wrote a letter to me
Suggesting I should take more vitamin D,
They said it would be good for my health
Regardless of the amount of my wealth.

They promised that they would send to me,
And assured that there would not be a fee,
A supply of some vitamin pills
That would keep me safe from all my ills.

They said that for a while I won't get the sun,
Especially now that winters begun,
And so from now until warmer days
It will be vitamins that replace the sun's rays.

I really am grateful because I am old
And really suffer when I get a cold,
And as I may even get something worse,
It will save the expense of hiring a nurse.